# Contents

**1 Our world** .......... p. 6

**2 Out and about!** .......... p. 18

Culture 1 .......... p. 30

**3 Day and night** .......... p. 32

**4 At the gallery** .......... p. 44

Culture 2 .......... p. 56

**5 Come in!** .......... p. 58

**6 Sports Day** .......... p. 70

Culture 3 .......... p. 82

Story book cut-outs .......... p. 85

# OUR WORLD

### INTRO:
Here we stand: children of every age,
This is our world and the world's our stage.
We can laugh, we can cry – we can float, we can fly,
We can dance, we can sing – we can do almost anything
in OUR world ... our *beautiful* world.

### VERSE 1:
Some of us are small; some of us are tall,
Some of us are shy; some say hi to everybody,
Some of us like numbers; some of us love words,
Some of us watch football, and some of us watch the birds!

### (CHORUS)
**This is our world** ... we're different but the same.
We live and learn together – we get to know each other ...
in OUR world ... our *beautiful* world.

### VERSE 2:
Some of us like music; some of us like cars,
Some of us draw pictures, looking at the stars,
Some of us are scientists, trying to find the code,
All of us can help a friend and give a hand to hold.

**This is our world** – there's room for everyone.
We learn to live together, and we have a lot of fun ...
In **our** world ... in **our** world ... in our beautiful world!

# Progress Chart

| You did it! | Congratulations! |
|---|---|

Unit 6

Unit 5

Unit 4

Unit 3

Unit 2

Unit 1

Creativity — Collaboration

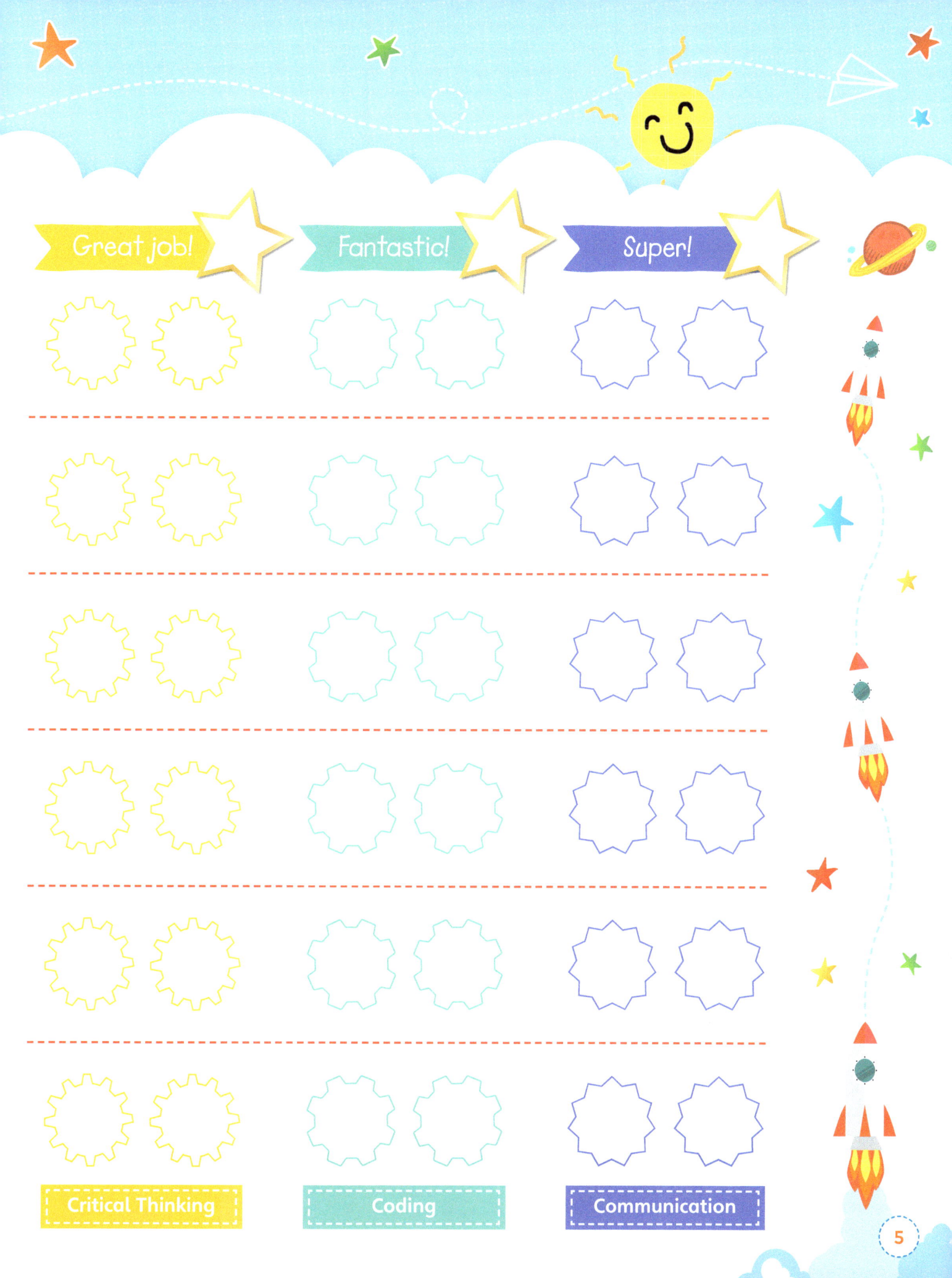

# 1 Our world

How can I create a nature scrapbook?

**1 Look, choose, and write.**

bridge   down   up

_____    _____    _____

**2 Choose and write.**

## CODE CRACKER

bat   bird   owl   porcupine   river   rock   snake   sun

| I look up! | I look down! |
|---|---|
| I can see a / an / the … ||
| _____  _____ | _____  _____ |
| _____  _____ | _____  _____ |

**3 Choose and complete. Then listen and check.**

The trees are g_____ .        Don't look d_____ .
The sky is b_____ .           Look, look at the sky!
I'm having fun in the trees with The t_____ are high.
y_____ !                      The s_____ is, too.
Climb up, climb u_____ .      I'm having f_____ in the
Climb up, climb very high!       trees with y_____ !

# Are you up in a tree?

VOCABULARY

*I will learn nature and direction words.*

## 1 Do the crossword.

bridge   flower   forest   hill   path   rock   tree

Across →

Down ↓

## EXTRA VOCABULARY

## 2 Look, listen, and say. Then match.

waterfall

lake

island

**I can** use nature and direction words.

# Language lab 1

**GRAMMAR 1: WALK / DON'T WALK**

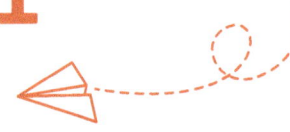

*I will understand and give instructions.*

## 1 Choose and write.

> Don't turn left   Don't turn right   Go straight   Turn left   Turn right

1 _____   2 _____   3 _____

4 _____   5 _____

## 2 Follow, find, and write.

### CODE CRACKER

a farm
b school
c store
d museum
e library
f playground
g swimming pool
h café

You are here

**Where are you?**

1 Go straight 5 blocks. ____

2 Go straight 7 blocks, turn left, go straight 3 blocks. ____

3 Go straight 6 blocks, turn right, go straight 2 blocks. ____

4 Go straight 8 blocks, turn right, go straight 4 blocks. ____

## 3 How do you get there? Look at 2. Circle and write.

Go   straight   Turn

**1** The swimming pool

Go _____ for ☐ blocks.
Turn  left / right . _____
straight for ☐ blocks.

**2** The museum

Go _____ for ☐ blocks.
_____ left / right .
_____ straight for ☐ blocks.

## 4 Now add more letters to 2 and tell a partner where to go.

Go straight for … blocks. Turn … . Where are you?

## 5 Make a stop sign. Then play the *Dance! Stop!* game.

Dance, jump, turn left, dance … STOP!

**I can** understand and give instructions.

# Story lab

**READING**

*I will read a story about helping others.*

**1** Look, choose, and complete.

bridge   forest   that   This

1. Wow! _____ is an amazing _____ !

Look at _____ _____ !

bridge   going   Me   on   too

I'm _____ the _____ !

2. I'm _____ up!

_____ _____ !

castle   fantastic   farm   our   school

3. It's _____ here!

I can see _____ _____ !

And the _____ and the _____ !

**2** Which words are in the story? Check ✓ or cross ✗.

goat ☐        house ☐
down ☐        fantastic ☐
forest ☐      up ☐
trampoline ☐  amazing ☐
cake ☐        farm ☐

## 3 Order and write.

1  Milly!  ,  done  Well
_____

2  now  down  !  Come
_____

3  !  the  Get  trampoline
_____

4  jump  with  Let's  Milly!
_____

## 4 Read and check ☑.

| Who ... | The children | Milly | Miss Kelly | Mrs. Hay | Mr. Mud |
|---|---|---|---|---|---|
| likes the forest? | | | | | |
| climbs up? | | | | | |
| climbs down? | | | | | |
| has lots of food? | | | | | |
| jumps down? | | | | | |
| jumps on the trampoline? | | | | | |
| helps Milly? | | | | | |

## 5 Look, read, and circle.

Milly / Mrs. Hay has lots of food.
She has bread / rice and apples /
cheese and cookies / ice cream .
The children are very happy / sad .

## 6 What happens next? ➡ page 91

**I can** read a story about helping others.

# Phonics lab

S, SH, J, AND CH

I will learn the **s**, **sh**, **j**, and **ch** sounds.

**1** Say the words. Then circle.

1   2   3   4

j  ch  s  sh      sh  ch  s  j      s  j  ch  sh      s  sh  j  ch

**2** Write **ch**, **sh**, **s**, or **j** and match.

1 ____icken ☐
2 ____op ☐
3 ____ell ☐
4 ____eese ☐
5 ____uice ☐
6 ____oup ☐

**3** Choose and write. Then listen and chant.

jump (x4)   shoes   sun

I have new _____ !

I can _____ !

_____ , _____ , _____

in the _____ !

**I can** use the **s**, **sh**, **j**, and **ch** sounds.

12

# Experiment lab

SCIENCE: LANDFORMS

*I will learn about landforms.*

## 1 Circle T (True) or F (False).

1  Our world has water and land.            T / F
2  Land is made of rocks.                   T / F
3  Rocks are always the same color.         T / F
4  Hills and mountains are made of water.   T / F
5  Tectonic plates are rocks.               T / F
6  Tectonic plates are above the earth.     T / F

# EXPERIMENT TIME

## Report

### 1 Answer for you. Write and circle.

1  How many towels do you have?  _____
2  Do you push the towels?        Yes / No
3  Do the towels go up?           Yes / No

### 2 Draw your towel mountains. Then choose for you and write.

don't look like   don't move
look like         move

I think the towels _____ mountains.

Tectonic plates _____ .

**I know** about landforms.

# Language lab 2

**GRAMMAR 2: ON, IN, UNDER, NEXT TO, BEHIND ...**

> I will use words to describe where things are.

## 1 Choose and write.

behind   in   next to   on   under

1 _____   2 _____   3 _____   4 _____   5 _____

## 2 Where are they? Do the math. Then choose and write.

**MATH ZONE**

35 + 35 = _____   25 × 4 = _____   8 × 5 = _____   15 × 2 = _____

behind   bridge   in   on   rock   tree   under

1  The rabbit is _____ the _____.

2  The cat is _____ the _____.

3  The lizard is _____ the _____.

4  The bird is _____ the _____.

**I can** use words to describe where things are.

# Draw a forest!

COMMUNICATION

I will understand and give instructions to play a game.

**1**  **Listen, draw, and match.**

## CODE CRACKER

**2** Work with a partner. Choose and tell them where to draw four more things.

- a river
- a fish
- a donkey
- a girl
- a boy
- a bridge
- a hill
- a path

Draw a donkey!

Okay. Where?

Next to the big tree.

**3** Now play the *True or false game* with your partner.

In my picture, the fish is in the small tree!

False!

**I can** understand and give instructions to play a game.

# PROJECT AND REVIEW UNIT 1

Make a nature scrapbook

Project report

## 1 Write and check ✓ or cross ✗ for your scrapbook.

|  | What's it called? | A photo | A drawing | A real thing |
|---|---|---|---|---|
| flower |  |  |  |  |
| tree |  |  |  |  |
| bird |  |  |  |  |
| animal |  |  |  |  |
| _____ |  |  |  |  |

## 2 Read and circle for you.

I like / don't like taking photos.

I like / don't like drawing animals / birds / flowers .

I like / don't like learning the names of trees.

## 3 Draw your favorite thing. Then write and circle.

It's a sunflower.
It's yellow.
It's near my school.
It's beautiful!

What is it? _____

What color is it? _____

Where is it? _____

I think it's fantastic / beautiful / amazing / wonderful .

**I can** make a nature scrapbook.

## 4 Circle 8 words. Then find and underline them in 5.

bridge jumping down up tree hill river mountain

## 5 Look, read, and match.

My name's Alicia. I'm having fun with my family and friends.

a

b

c

d

1 Look at me! I'm in a tree! I'm climbing up the tree.

2 I'm walking on a bridge with my family. The bridge is an old tree! It's above the river.

3 I'm jumping with my friends. We're on a hill. Jump, jump, jump!

4 Look at my sister! She's going down a mountain! She's very happy!

## 6 Read and complete to describe pictures in 5. Use words from 4.

a The _____ is above the _____ .

b Alicia and her friends are _____ on a _____ .

c Alicia is climbing _____ the _____ .

d Alicia's sister is going _____ a _____ .

Now go to your progress chart on page 4.

# 2 Out and about!

### How can I create a town guide?

**1**  **Look, match, and circle.**

castle / café     swimming pool / café     castle / swimming pool

**2 Circle the odd one out.**

## CODE CRACKER

1 café   a   b    c

2 swimming pool   a   b    c

3 castle   a   b    c

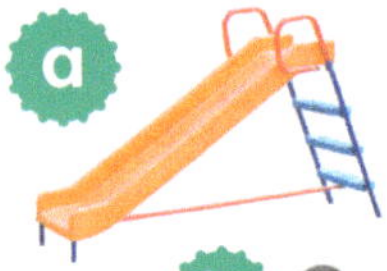

**3**  **Listen to the song. Number the words in order.**

school ☐    stores ☐    pool ☐    castle ☐

# Where are they?

**VOCABULARY**

*I will learn town words.*

## 1 Label the pictures.

1 _____  2 _____  3 _____  4 _____

## 2 Unscramble the words.

1 féac _____
3 marf _____
5 yabrilr _____
7 kapr _____
9 erriv _____
11 ostre _____

2 tclase _____
4 suhoe _____
6 usemum _____
8 unlapydrog _____
10 coolsh _____
12 wingsmim loop _____

**EXTRA VOCABULARY**

## 3 🎧 007 Listen and say. Then match.

hotel

mall

zoo

 a

 c

 b

**I can** use town words.

# Language lab 1

**GRAMMAR 1: LIKE / DON'T LIKE**

I will talk about town words using *like / don't like*.

## 1 Look, read, and match.

- She doesn't like cafés.
- He likes museums.

- He doesn't like farms.
- She likes school.

## 2 Circle and write likes or doesn't like.

1  He / She _____ libraries. (Tom)
2  He / She _____ castles. (Monica)
3  He / She _____ stores. (Kate)
4  He / She _____ swimming pools. (Mark)

## 3 Look, listen, and check ☑.

1  Ben          2  Carla          3  Sam          4  Jenny

a 😀 ☐          a 😀 ☐          a 😀 ☐          a 😀 ☐
b 🙁 ☐          b 🙁 ☐          b 🙁 ☐          b 🙁 ☐

## 4 Read and write . or ? Then circle.

1  Does Ben like school ____           Yes, he does.  /  No, he doesn't.
2  Carla doesn't like the castle ____   True  /  False
3  Sam likes the river ____             True  /  False
4  Does Jenny like the café ____        Yes, she does.  /  No, she doesn't.

## 5 Draw 😀 or ☹ for you. Then choose and write.

Yes, I do.   No, I don't.   like   don't like

Do you like libraries?
_____
I _____ libraries.

Do you like school?
_____
I _____ school.

Do you like stores?
_____
I _____ stores.

## 6  Make. Then show and tell.

I like cats and cars!

I don't like frogs and pears!

**I can** talk about town words using  like  /  don't like .

# Story lab

READING

*I will read a story about a town.*

## A special day

**1** Make your story book. → page 85

1 Order and write the page numbers.
2 Complete the story.
3 Draw a cover.
4 Complete the story review.

**2** Order and write.

like   castle!   the   I

1 _____

a   We   cake!   big   have

2 _____

know!   don't   I

3 _____

Town!   birthday,   Happy   Castle

4 _____

**3** Choose and color. Then write and say.

black   blue   brown   green   orange
pink   purple   red   yellow

What color is your castle?

My castle is _____.

# 4 Read and match.

1. What's happening, Leo?
2. Where are Anna and Leo?
3. Thank you!

- You're welcome!
- I don't know!
- We're here, Miss Kelly!

# 5 Count and write numbers and words.

**MATH ZONE**

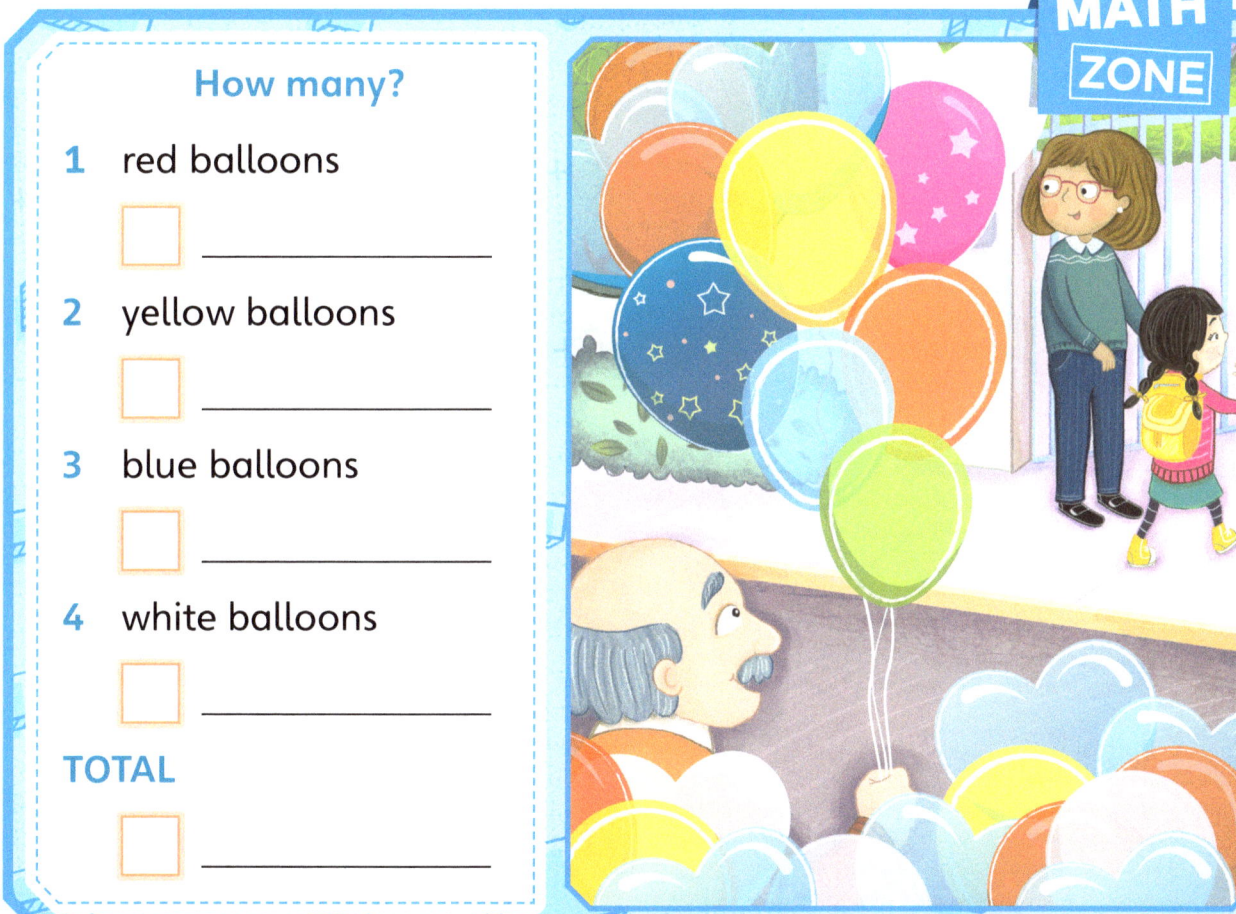

**How many?**

1. red balloons ☐ _____
2. yellow balloons ☐ _____
3. blue balloons ☐ _____
4. white balloons ☐ _____

TOTAL ☐ _____

**I can** read a story about a town.

# Phonics lab
A AND E

I will learn the a and e sounds.

**1** Circle 6 words.

cappegbagmatwetten

**2** Write a or e. Then look and match.

1. c __ p ☐
2. p __ g ☐
3. b __ g ☐
4. m __ t ☐
5. w __ t ☐
6. t __ n ☐

a

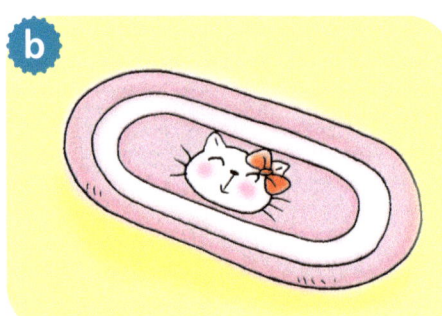
b

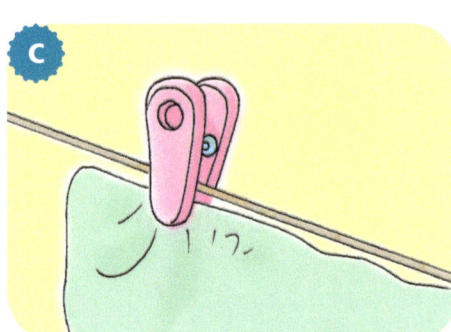
c

d

e

f

**3** Read, listen, and circle.

1. mat / wet
2. cap / ten
3. peg / cap
4. mat / peg
5. bag / wet
6. bag / ten

**I can** use the a and e sounds.

# Experiment lab

ENGINEERING: HOW TO BUILD A HOUSE

*I will learn about building materials.*

## 1 💡 Match, choose, and write.

bricks   cement   steel   wood

1 _____ ☐   2 _____ ☐

3 _____ ☐   4 _____ ☐

  a

  b

  c

  d

## 2 How many bricks do you need? Draw and write.

**MATH ZONE**

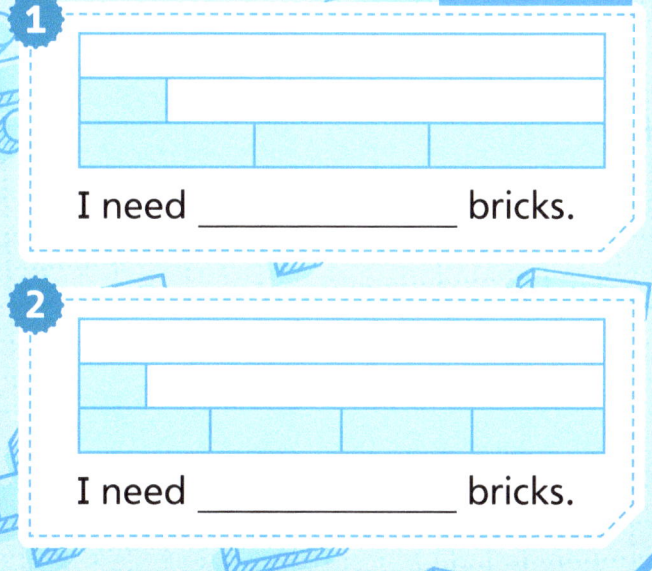

1  I need _____ bricks.

2  I need _____ bricks.

## EXPERIMENT TIME

### Report

**1 Draw a tower.**

**2 Read and circle for you.**

My tower is made of  cups  /  clay  / spaghetti  /  construction paper .

My tower is  strong  /  not strong !

**I know** about building materials.

# Language lab 2

**GRAMMAR 2: THERE IS / THERE ARE**

I will describe places using there is / there are.

## 1 Read and draw.

I like this village! There's a castle! There are three houses and four stores. There's a museum and there are two rivers!

## 2 Look and say.

There are ten stores.    Picture b!

## 3 Circle and write about Picture b.

> There's   There are   houses   library

1. There's / There are a pool.
2. There's / There are ten stores.
3. There's / There are a farm.
4. _____ two cafés.
5. There's a _____ .
6. _____ five _____ .

 **I can** use there is / there are .

# Let's play!

COMMUNICATION

 I will talk about games.

**1** 🎧 010 **Look, listen, and number.**

a

b

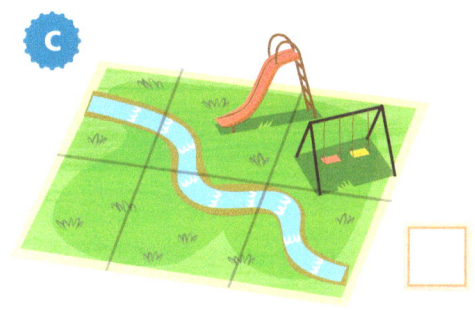
c

**2 Read and match. Then circle game a, b, or c.**

1. There are lots of horses and a farm! / Me too! / I like it.
   a   b   c

2. It's great! Let's make the castle. / Good idea.
   a   b   c

3. Let's play this game. There's a park. / This is my favorite! / Oh, look! There's a river, too.
   a   b   c

**3** 💬 **Talk about this game with a partner.**

café   castle   farm
house   library
museum   park
playground   river
school   store
swimming pool

**I can** talk about games.

27

# PROJECT AND REVIEW UNIT 2

Make a town guide

Project report

**1** Check ☑ or cross ☒ and write for your town guide.

|  | Photo | Drawing | Writing |
|---|---|---|---|
| My school |  |  |  |
| My house |  |  |  |
| A museum |  |  |  |
| A river |  |  |  |
| A farm |  |  |  |
| _____ |  |  |  |

**2** Choose, complete, and circle for your town.

> castle(s)   farm(s)   house(s)   museum(s)   school(s)   store(s)

1  There's a _____ . I like / don't like the _____ .
2  There's a _____ . I like / don't like the _____ .
3  There are _____ . I like / don't like the _____ .

**3** 💬 Ask and answer about your partner's favorite place.

What's your favorite place in town?

There is / There are … . I like the … .

**I can** make a town guide.

28

## 4 Look at the photos. Read and check ✓ T (True) or F (False).

I'm Donny. This is my town.

| | T | F |
|---|---|---|
| 1 There's a farm. | ☐ | ☐ |
| 2 There are four houses. | ☐ | ☐ |
| 3 There isn't a swimming pool. | ☐ | ☐ |
| 4 There are two museums. | ☐ | ☐ |
| 5 There aren't any stores. | ☐ | ☐ |

## 5 Read, listen, and circle.

1 Donny  likes / doesn't like  the museum.
2 He  likes / doesn't like  the castle.
3 He  likes / doesn't like  the cafés.

## 6 Now talk to a partner about Donny's town.

Do you like the museum?

Now go to your progress chart on page 4.

# Beautiful gardens

CULTURE 1

**1. Choose, complete, and match.**

beautiful   city   garden
giants   rock   walls

1  Some people grow flowers on roofs and _____ .
2  This _____ is in England.
3  There are _____ in this garden.
4  This garden is in a big _____ , Singapore.
5  Plants make cities look _____ .
6  The giants are made of _____ .

## 2 Read and check ✓ T (True) or F (False).

|   | T | F |
|---|---|---|
| 1 The giants have hair made of leaves and grass. | ☐ | ☐ |
| 2 The Lost Gardens of Heligan are not old. | ☐ | ☐ |
| 3 There are no gardens in Singapore. | ☐ | ☐ |
| 4 Plants, trees, and flowers make oxygen. | ☐ | ☐ |

# 3 Day and night
How can I talk about day and night?

**1 Look, read, and write a or b.**

It's day.   It's night.

1  There's a porcupine and it's dark.   ____
2  There's a donkey and it's light.   ____
3  There's an owl, a bat, and a fox.   ____

a

b

**2 Read and color.**

## CODE CRACKER

1

Look at the owl. It's night. The sky is black. The moon is white.

2

Look at the donkey. It's day. The sky is blue. The sun is yellow.

**3  Read and circle. Then listen and order.**

a  At night, at night, the owl / I  wakes up.  ☐
b  In the day, in the day, I  sleep / wake up .  ☐
c  At night, at night, I  sleep / wake up .  ☐
d  In the day, in the day, he  sleep / sleeps .  ☐

32

# What is it?

**VOCABULARY**

*I will learn animal and daily routine words.*

## CODE CRACKER

**1** What comes next? Circle the picture and write.

1  cow   donkey   cow   donkey          _____ 
2  bat   owl   owl   bat                 _____  
3  goat   goat   porcupine   goat        _____ 
4  bat   bat   cow   cow                 _____ 
5  porcupine   porcupine   donkey   donkey      _____ 
6  donkey   donkey   goat   donkey       _____

**EXTRA VOCABULARY**

**2** 🎧 Listen and say. Then match.

1  deer

2  snake

3  wolf

a

b

c

**I can** use animal and daily routine words.

33

# Language lab 1

**GRAMMAR 1: I GO / DON'T GO**

*I will talk about daily routines.*

## 1 Circle, choose, and complete.

brush   go   go   wake

1   I / We _____ to school.
2   I / We _____ to school.
3   I / We _____ our teeth.
4   I / We _____ up.

## 2 Order for you.

brush my teeth   eat   go to school   sleep   wake up   wash my face

 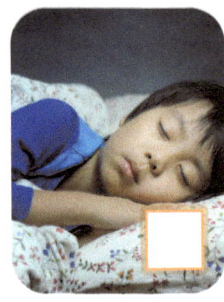    

## 3 Listen and circle.

1   Do you wash your hands at school?     Yes, I do. / No, I don't.
2   Do you eat at school?                  Yes, I do. / No, I don't.
3   Do you brush your teeth at school?     Yes, I do. / No, I don't.
4   Do you sleep at school?                Yes, I do. / No, I don't.

## 4 Complete for you.

1  wake up           I ____don't wake up____ in the playground.
2  sleep             I _____ in the library.
3  eat               I _____ at home.
4  wash my hands     I _____ at the café.
5  brush my teeth    I _____ in the swimming pool.

## 5 Read and check ✓ T (True) or F (False). Then say.

1  Cows eat pizza.
2  Bats sleep in the day.
3  Porcupines go to school.
4  Goats brush their teeth.
5  Donkeys eat grass.
6  Owls wash their hands.

Cows don't eat pizza!

## 6 Make cards and play the *Do you …?* game.

Do you eat in the swimming pool?

No, I don't!

**I can** talk about daily routines.

# Story lab

READING

> I will read a story about farm animals.

## Do goats dance?

**1** ⚗ **Make your story book.** → page 87

1. Order and write the page numbers.
2. Complete the story.
3. Draw a cover.
4. Complete the story review.

**2 Read and match.**

1. Do cows sing?
2. Do goats dance, Miss Kelly?
3. Hello, Mrs. Hay. What's happening?

- I don't know.
- No, Tom! They don't sing. They say "moo!"
- No, Tom! They don't dance!

**3 Join the dots. Then choose and complete.**

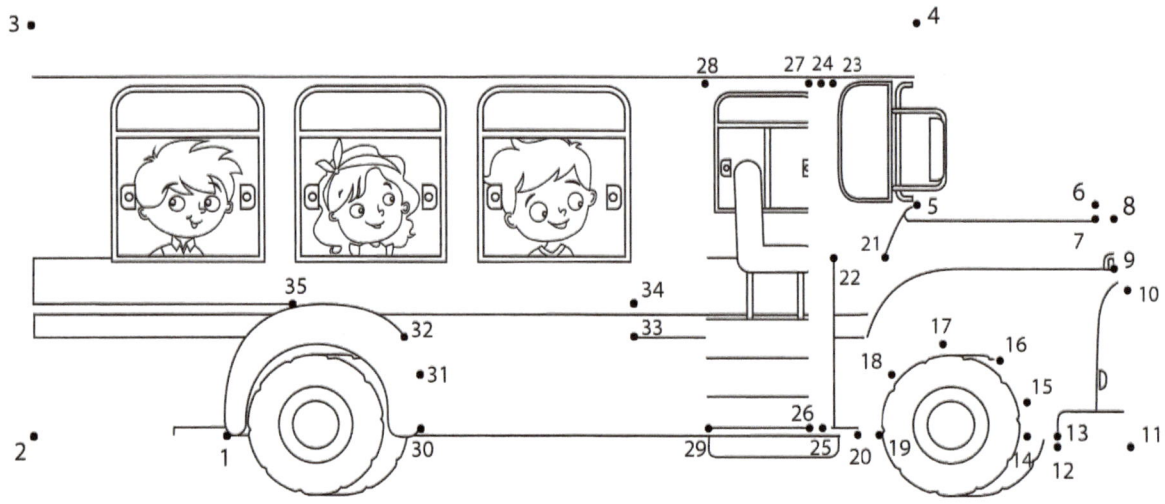

at Mrs. Hay's farm    at school    on the bus

Anna, Leo, and Tom are _____ .

## 4 Order and write.

1  music   !   They   the   like

_____

2  is   cow   .   a   This

_____

## 5 Find, count, and write.

1  There are _____ cows.
2  There are _____ sheep.
3  There are _____ donkeys.
4  There are _____ goats.
5  There are _____ animals.

## 6 Now do the math.

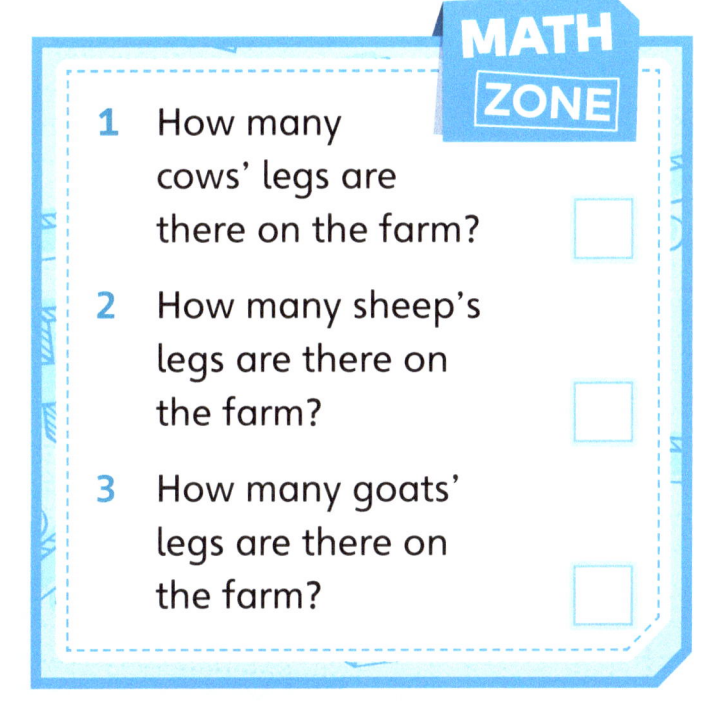

**MATH ZONE**

1  How many cows' legs are there on the farm?

2  How many sheep's legs are there on the farm?

3  How many goats' legs are there on the farm?

## 7 What happens next? Check ✓ and draw your idea.

The animals go to school.

The animals sleep.

The animals eat grass.

**I can** read a story about farm animals.

37

# Phonics lab

I AND O

*I will learn the i and o sounds.*

**1 Circle and write the words with the i sound.**

| British | American |
|---|---|
| bin | trash can |

| h | a | t | o | b | e | k |
|---|---|---|---|---|---|---|
| i | c | p | d | n | l | p |
| t | r | b | i | n | v | g |
| s | i | x | g | i | m | z |
| w | g | n | o | s | u | i |
| r | t | y | j | x | h | q |

1  _____   2  _____

3  _____   4  _____

**2 Write o and match.**

1  j____g

2  f____x

3  h____t

**3 Read, listen, and write i or o.**

1  S____x l____ttle ch____ldren s____t and s____ng.

2  St____p the fr____g!

**I can** use the i and o sounds.

# Experiment lab

SCIENCE: THE SUN AND THE EARTH

*I will learn about the earth and the sun.*

## 1 Label the picture.

day    earth    night    sun

1 _____
2 _____
3 _____
4 _____

## 2 Look, read, and match.

1  24 hours        • 1 year •

2  12 months       • 1 day •

# EXPERIMENT TIME

## Report

**1** Write your report. Check ✓ the correct picture and complete the sentence.

earth    sun

The _____ goes around the _____.

**I know** about the earth and the sun.

# Language lab 2

**GRAMMAR 2: SHE EATS / DOESN'T EAT**

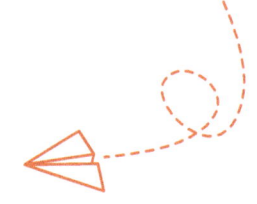

*I will ask and answer about daily routines.*

## 1 Look and say.

**It's Saturday! What do they do?**

My name is Megan.

She eats an apple.

My name is Danny.

He goes to the museum.

## 2 Choose and write answers.

No, he doesn't.  No, she doesn't.  Yes, he does.  Yes, she does.

1  Does Megan go to school on Saturday?  _____
2  Does she brush her teeth?  _____
3  Does Danny go to the library on Saturday?  _____
4  Does he wash his hands?  _____

## 3 Circle and write about Megan or Danny.

eats   doesn't eat   doesn't go   goes

It's Saturday!  He / She _____ to school.

He / She _____ to the museum / library .

He / She _____ an apple / a banana .

**I can** ask and answer about daily routines.

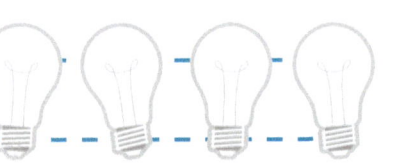

# What time is it?

**COMMUNICATION**

I will ask and answer about time and daily routines.

**1** 🎧 016  **Listen and circle. Then match.**

1. It's seven / five o'clock. ☐
2. It's twelve / three o'clock. ☐
3. It's four / eleven o'clock. ☐
4. It's eight / ten o'clock. ☐

a  b  c  d

**2** 💬 **What time do you wake up? Talk to a partner.**

I wake up at seven o'clock on Monday.

**3** 💬 **Ask and answer with a partner. Then circle Yes or No.**

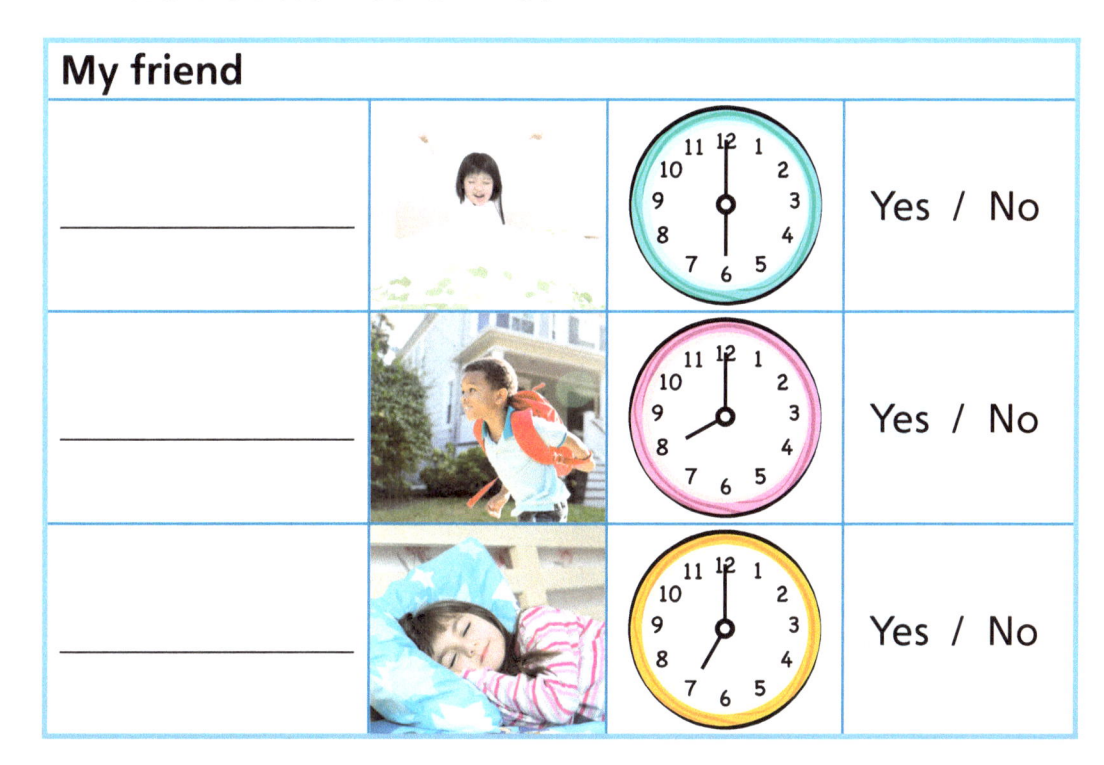

| My friend | | | |
|---|---|---|---|
| _____ | | | Yes / No |
| _____ | | | Yes / No |
| _____ | | | Yes / No |

Do you wake up at six o'clock on Saturday?

No, I don't. I wake up at seven o'clock.

**4** 💬 **Now tell the class.**

**I can** ask and answer about time and daily routines.

# PROJECT AND REVIEW UNIT 3

Do a day and night presentation

**Project report**

## 1. Check ✓ or cross ✗ for your presentation.

|  | I have pictures of … | I talk about … | I write about … |
|---|---|---|---|
| The sun | | | |
| The moon | | | |
| Animals | | | |
| Me | | | |
| A friend | | | |
| My school | | | |
| _____ | | | |

## 2. Draw, choose, and write.

wake up / sleep / eat    wakes up / sleeps / eats

**1**
- ☀ In the day, I _____ .
- ☾ At night, I _____ .

**2**
- ☀ It _____ .
- ☾ It _____ .

_A bat_

_It sleeps._

I can do a day and night presentation.

**3** Write one thing you say in your presentation.

**4** Look, read, and circle T (True) or F (False).

1. I wake up at six o'clock.        T / F
2. I eat an orange every day.       T / F
3. I don't brush my teeth at night. T / F
4. I go to school at nine o'clock.  T / F

I'm Ken.

**5** Look, listen, and circle.

1. Stella wakes up at
   a    b

2. She eats
   a    b

3. She goes to school at
   a    b

This is my friend, Stella.

**6** Now talk to a partner about Ken and Stella.

Does Ken wake up at five o'clock?

No, he doesn't.

Now go to your progress chart on page 4.

# 4 At the gallery

How can I create a portrait gallery?

**1** Circle a, b, or c. Then point and say.

**CODE CRACKER**

1. happy  sad  angry   a  b  c
2. angry  sad  happy   a  b  c
3. happy  angry  sad   a  b  c

**2** Think. Then choose for you and say.   angry  happy  sad

I look at this picture and I am …

**3** Listen to the song and order.

shy ☐   happy ☐   kind ☐   angry ☐

# I am happy!

**VOCABULARY**

> I will learn describing words for people and pets.

## 1 Look, read, and number.

1 helpful   2 friendly   3 kind   4 angry   5 happy   6 sad

## 2 Read, color, and write the names.

**CODE CRACKER**

Tina has a red T-shirt. She is funny!

Maria has a yellow T-shirt. She is shy.

Billy has a blue T-shirt. He is tired.

**EXTRA VOCABULARY**

## 3 Listen and say. Then match.

1  sporty         • Good morning. How are you today?
2  chatty         • Hi! Hello! Do you like English? Me too! Let's talk!
3  polite         • I can climb!

**I can** use words for describing people and pets.

# Language lab 1

GRAMMAR 1: HE / SHE   IS / ISN'T

> I will describe people using **always / sometimes / never**.

**1** Follow and order the jumbled letters for each person. Then write **He's** or **She's**.

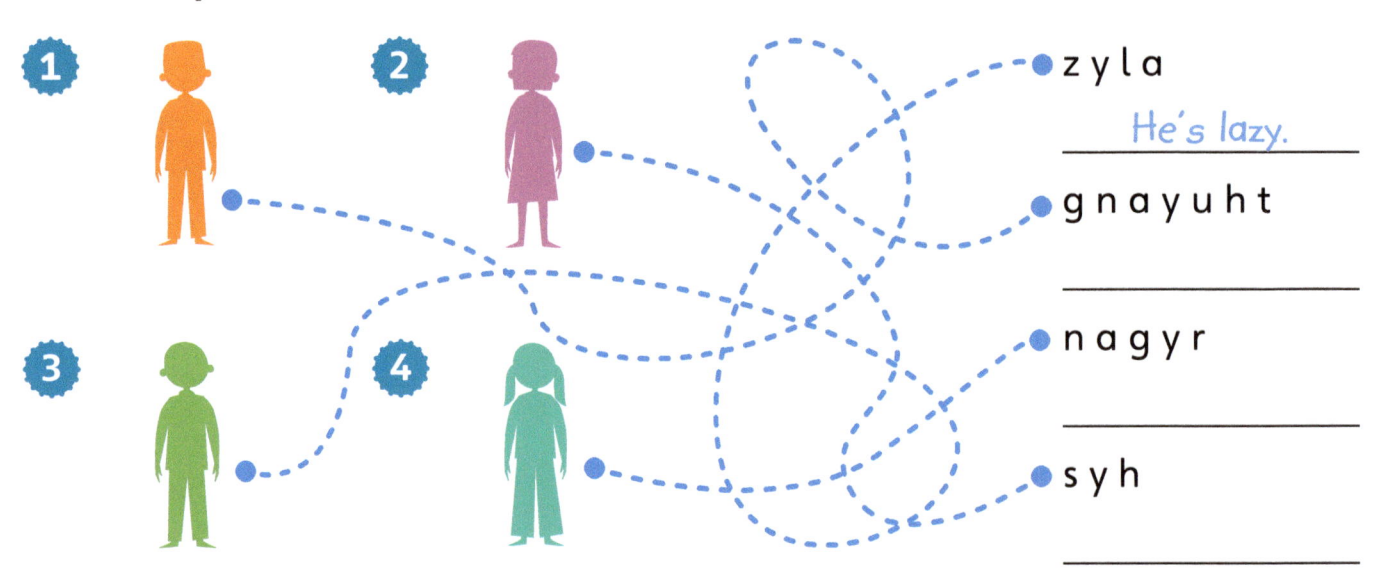

- z y l a
  _He's lazy._
- g n a y u h t
  _____
- n a g y r
  _____
- s y h
  _____

**2** Look, read, and write.

> No, he isn't.   No, she isn't.   Yes, he is.   Yes, she is.

1  Is he young?      _____
2  Is he friendly?   _____
3  Is she helpful?   _____
4  Is she old?       _____

**3** Look and write **He is** or **He isn't**.

1  _____ friendly.
2  _____ angry.
3  _____ kind.
4  _____ naughty.

## 4 Circle, choose, and write.

always   never   sometimes

1   He / She is _____ funny.

2   He / She is _____ helpful.

3   He / She is _____ sad.

## 5 Make a word picture. Draw and write about a friend or someone in your family.

## 6 Now show and tell.

This is my brother. He's sometimes naughty! He's always funny.

HAPPY FRIENDLY NAUGHTY FUN NAUGHTY FUNNY HAPPY FRIENDLY
THIS IS MY BROTHER

**I can** use always / sometimes / never.

# Story lab

**READING**

> I will read a story about a painting competition.

## Who is this?

### 1. Make your story book. → page 89

1. Order and write the page numbers.
2. Complete the story.
3. Draw a cover.
4. Complete the story review.

### 2. Look, read, and match.

1. Who is this, Tom?
2. Who is this, Mrs. Hay?
3. The gold cup goes to … Mr. Mud!

- Congratulations, Mr. Mud!
- It's my friend.
- It's my cousin. He's sometimes naughty and always happy!

### 3. Choose, complete, and match.

crayons   paints   pencils   photo

1. I have a _____ !
2. I have _____ and _____ . 
3. I have my _____ . 

48

## 4 Check ✓ T (True) or F (False).

|   | T | F |
|---|---|---|
| 1 Mrs. Hay paints her friend. | ☐ | ☐ |
| 2 Tom paints his brother. | ☐ | ☐ |
| 3 Mr. Mud paints Milly. | ☐ | ☐ |
| 4 Milly paints Mr. Mud. | ☐ | ☐ |

## 5 Work with a partner. Point, ask, and answer.

Who is this?

It's Anna. That's her nose.

## 6 What happens next? Choose, check ✓, and draw.

1 ☐ Milly is tired now!

2 ☐ Milly has the gold cup now!

3 ☐ Look! What a lovely rainbow!

**I can** read a story about a painting competition.

49

# Phonics lab

J AND Y

*I will learn the j and y sounds.*

## 1 Write j or y and match.

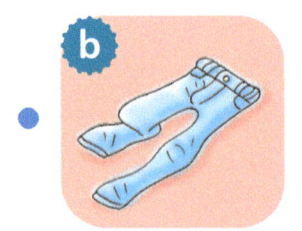

1. ____ump
2. ____es
3. ____o-____o
4. ____uice
5. ____oung
6. ____eans
7. ____ungle
8. ____ellow

a  b  c  d  e  f  g  h

## 2 Listen and circle.

1. jaguar / yogurt
2. yak / jar
3. yours / jeans
4. yellow / jungle

## 3 Write j or y and draw.

There's a ____aguar in the ____ungle! It's ____ellow and black.

**I can** use the j and y sounds.

# Experiment lab
ART AND DESIGN: CHANGING FACES

*I will learn about changing faces.*

## 1 Label the face.

eyebrow   eye color   lines   smile

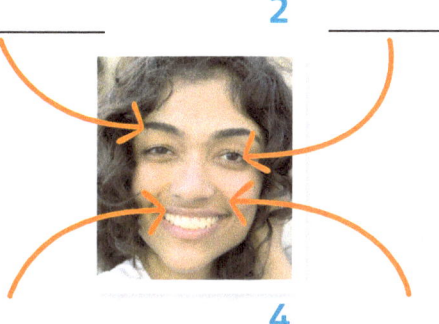

1 _____   2 _____
3 _____   4 _____

## 2 Read and circle.

a   b

1  She looks angry.       a / b
2  Her eyes look big.     a / b
3  Her mouth looks big.   a / b

## 3 Now talk to a partner.

Her eyes look small.

Picture b!

# EXPERIMENT TIME

## Report

**1** Look, read, and match.

1   2   3

cry    laugh    yawn

**2** Now write for you.

always   never   sometimes

In our experiment …

My partner laughs.
I _____ laugh.
My partner yawns.
I _____ yawn.
My partner cries.
I _____ cry.

**I know** about changing faces.

# Language lab 2

**GRAMMAR 2: DO YOU HAVE ...?**

*I will ask and answer about people and objects using have.*

## 1 Read, do the math, and color.

**MATH ZONE**

Do you have a dog? ☐

dog: nose = 15 + 2, body = 18 – 6

Do you have a mouse? ☐

mouse: nose = 12 + 7, body = 3 x 3

Do you have a cat? ☐

cat: nose = 20 – 3, body = 2 x 7

Do you have a rabbit? ☐

rabbit: nose = 20 – 1, body = 8 + 1

9 = gray    12 = brown    14 = orange    17 = black    19 = pink

## 2 Now check ✓ two animals from 1. Then ask and answer with a partner.

- Do you have a rabbit?
- No, I don't. / Yes, I do.
- What color is its nose?
- It's ...
- What color is its body?

**I can** ask and answer using **have**.

# Let's take a photo!

**COMMUNICATION**

*I will talk about funny photos.*

**1** 🔊 **Look, listen, and check ✓.**

1  a    b
2  a    b

**2** 💬 **Listen again and circle the sentences you hear. Act out with a partner.**

1  Let's take a photo!  /  Let's do a photo!

2  Okay … I can wait … I can look!  /  Okay … wait … look!

3  Oh, this is funny photo.  /  Oh, that's a funny photo.

**3** 💬 **Choose a picture. Draw your face. Then talk to a partner.**

Look at me!

Do you have a hat?

Yes, I do!

Are you happy?

**I can** talk about funny photos.

# PROJECT AND REVIEW  UNIT 4

Create a portrait gallery

**Project report**

**1** Write and check ✓ or cross ✗ for your gallery.

|  | Name | Painting | Drawing | Photo |
|---|---|---|---|---|
| Friend | | | | |
| Family | | | | |
| Teacher | | | | |
| Pet | | | | |
| _____ | | | | |

**2** Read and complete. Then check ✓ the questions you ask.

> Are   favorite   have
> old   sometimes

1  How _____ are you?
2  What's your _____ day?
3  _____ you happy today?
4  Are you _____ sad?
5  Do you _____ a pet?

**3** Draw and write about a friend's picture.

This picture is by Ava.
It's her mom.
She's always happy.

This picture is by _____.
It's _____.

I can create a portrait gallery.

## 4 Read and check ✓ the correct sentences.

**1**

a  This is my friend. He isn't happy. He's sad. ☐

b  This is my friend. He isn't sad. He's happy. ☐

c  This is my friend. She isn't sad. She's happy. ☐

**2**

a  This is my cousin. She isn't tired. She's angry. ☐

b  This is my cousin. He isn't angry. He's tired. ☐

c  This is my cousin. She isn't angry. She's tired. ☐

## 5 Listen and circle.

1  Do you have a pet?           Yes, I do.  /  No, I don't.
2  What's its name?              Lulu  /  Pepper
3  Are you sometimes shy?   Yes, I am.  /  No, I'm not.
4  What's your favorite color?  blue  /  purple

## 6 Now work with a partner. Ask and answer for you.

Now go to your progress chart on page 4.

# Music around the world
CULTURE 2

**1** Choose and write.

> bagpipes   drum   pipes   sticks   strings   veena

1. _____
2. _____
3. _____

**2** Read and circle.

1. The drums are  square / round .
2. The drums are  heavy / light .
3. The bagpipes have a  soft / hard  bag.
4. The pipes are  short / long .
5. The veena is  small / big .
6. The veena is  square / round .

**3** Draw a musical instrument from your country. Then write and circle.

This is a _____ .

It's _____ and _____ .

I  like / don't like  this instrument.

The music makes me feel  happy / sad / angry / tired .

# 5 Come in!

## How can I create a class meal?

**1** Look, read, and write a, b, or c.

1. I have pasta. I don't have cookies. ☐
2. I have cookies. I don't have pasta. ☐
3. I have pasta. I don't have cheese. ☐

**2** Look, choose, and write.

## CODE CRACKER

Come in!
Goodbye!
Thank you!

1. _____ 
2. _____ 
3. _____

**3** Listen to the song. Order. Write 1–4.

a. Would you like some cheese? ☐
b. Yes, please! ☐
c. Would you like some cookies? ☐
d. We're happy that you're here. ☐

# Do you like cookies?

**I will learn food words.**

VOCABULARY

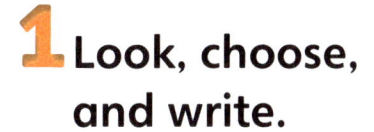

**1** Look, choose, and write.

> bread   cheese   chicken   cookies   fish   ice cream
> juice   pasta   rice   salad   soup   water

1 _____
2 _____
3 _____
4 _____
5 _____
6 _____
7 _____
8 _____
9 _____
10 _____
11 _____
12 _____

EXTRA VOCABULARY

**2** 🎧 💡 Listen and say. Then match.

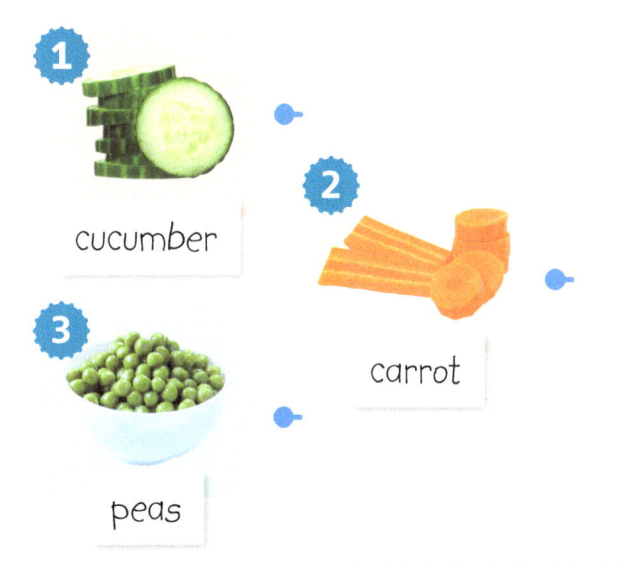

1 cucumber
2 carrot
3 peas

a
b
c

**I can** use food words.

# Language lab 1

**GRAMMAR 1: CAN I HAVE ...?**

*I will ask for things politely using Can I have ...?*

**1** Follow, circle, and write **Can I have some ..., please?**

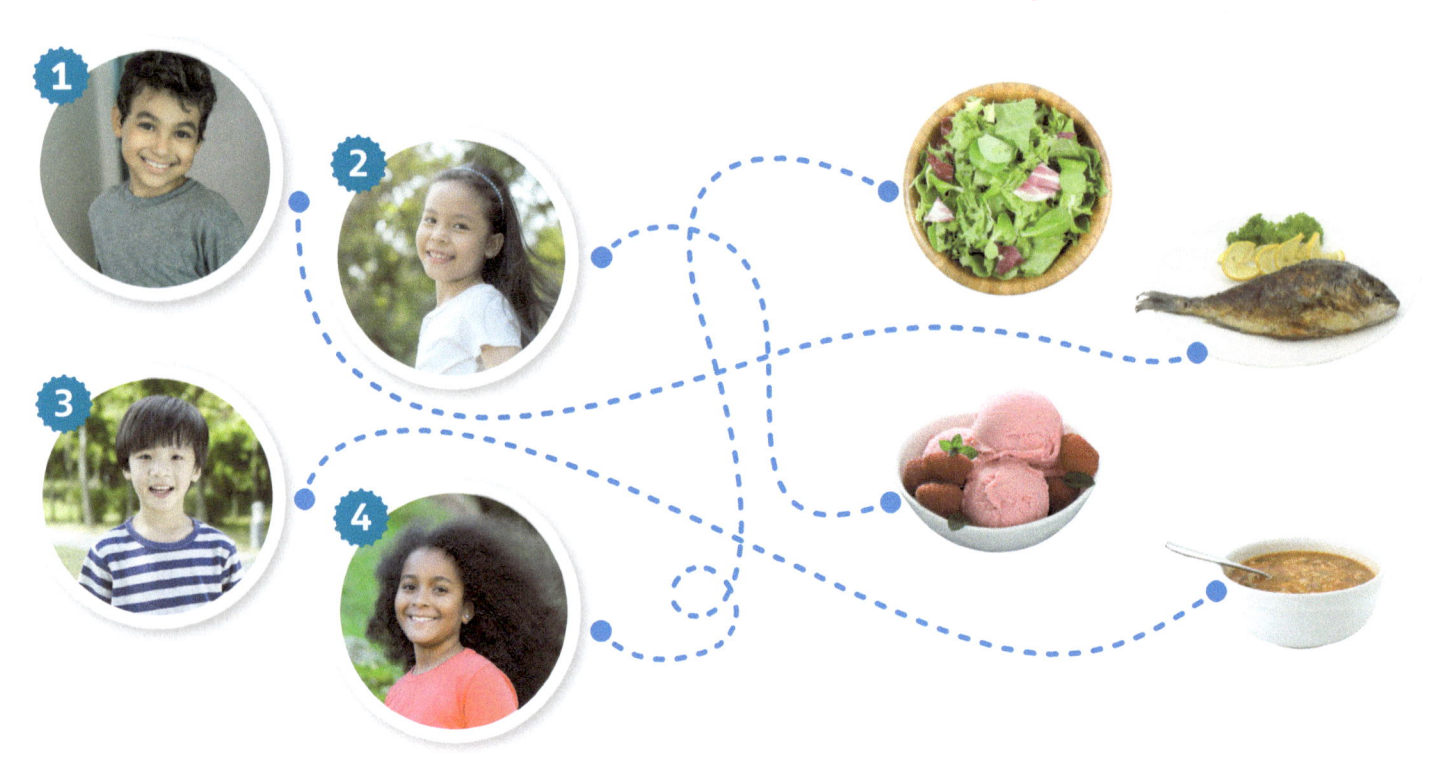

1 _____ fish / salad , _____ ?
2 _____ soup / ice cream , _____ ?
3 _____ salad / soup , _____ ?
4 _____ salad / ice cream , _____ ?

**2** Listen, number, and circle.

a                    b                    c                    d

Sure! / Sorry, no.   Sure! / Sorry, no.   Sure! / Sorry, no.   Sure! / Sorry, no.

60

## 3 Read and do the math. Then read and write Sure! or Sorry, no.

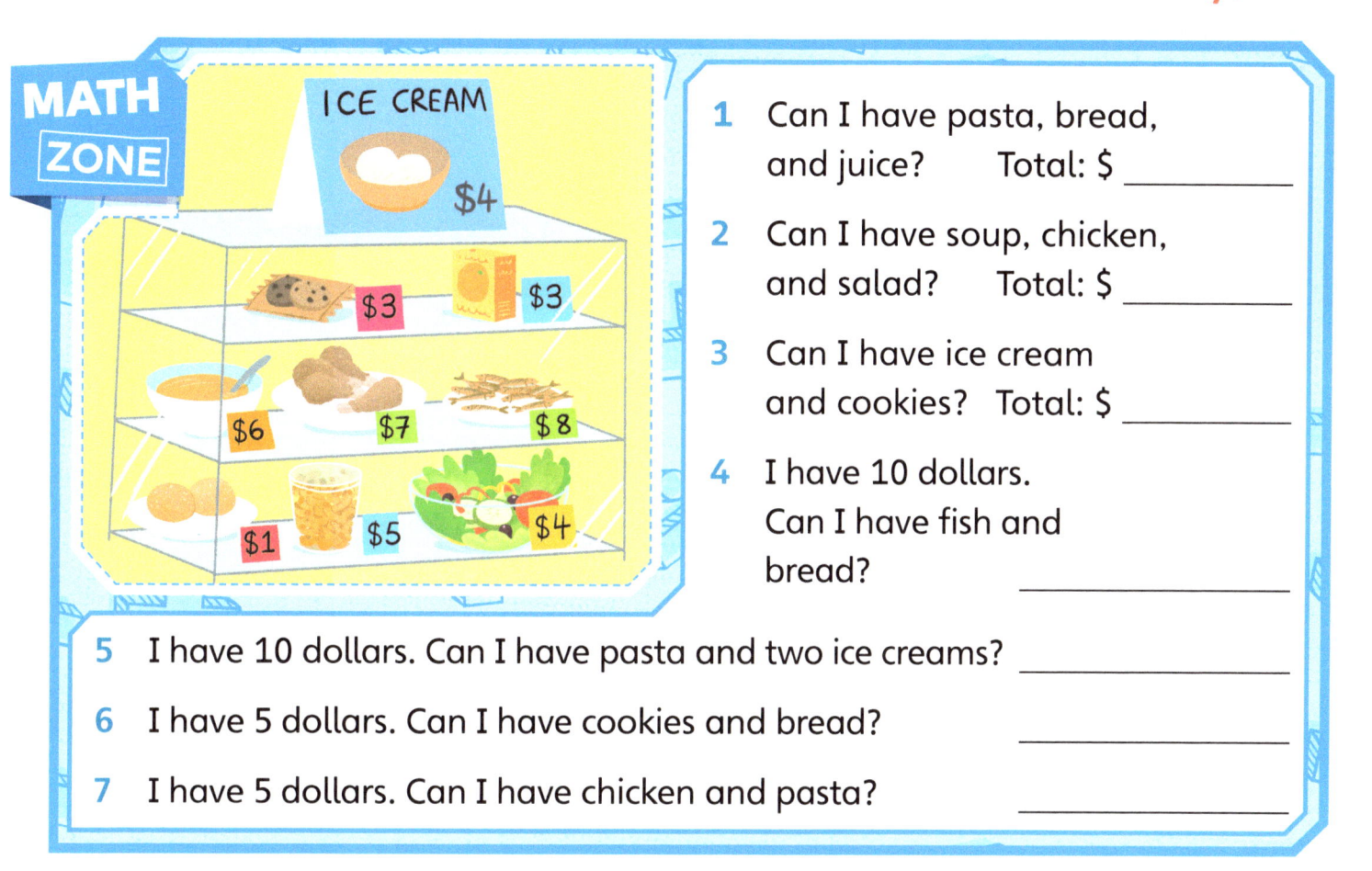

**MATH ZONE**

1. Can I have pasta, bread, and juice?  Total: $ _____
2. Can I have soup, chicken, and salad?  Total: $ _____
3. Can I have ice cream and cookies?  Total: $ _____
4. I have 10 dollars. Can I have fish and bread?  _____
5. I have 10 dollars. Can I have pasta and two ice creams?  _____
6. I have 5 dollars. Can I have cookies and bread?  _____
7. I have 5 dollars. Can I have chicken and pasta?  _____

ICE CREAM $4
$3  $3
$6  $7  $8
$1  $5  $4

## 4 Play the *Can I have …?* game with a partner.

PASTA   CHEESE   FISH

SALAD   SOUP   CHICKEN

## 5 Now play the *Spell and Ask* game with a partner.

Can I have c-h-i-c-k-i-n, please?

Sorry, no.

Can I have f-i-s-h, please?

Sure!

**I can** ask for things politely using Can I have …?

61

# Story lab

**READING**

> I will read a story about Tom's cousin.

## Come over and play!

**1** Look, choose, and complete.

---

Come  cousin  Grandma  here

**1** Tom, look! _____ and Aunt Julia are _____ ! And your _____ , Adam!

_____ in!

---

Can  course  have  please  some

**2** Can I _____ some water, _____ ?

_____ I have _____ juice, please?

Yes, of _____ !

---

Can  okay  this

**3** _____ I have _____ car?

Er … _____ .

---

book  dear  okay  sorry

**4** Oh _____ ! I'm _____ , Tom!

Can I have this _____ ?

Er … _____ .

62

## 2 Circle T (True) or F (False).

1. It's Sunday. T / F
2. Grandma, Aunt Julia, and Adam are at school. T / F
3. Tom has lots of toys. T / F
4. The book is for Adam. It is his book. T / F
5. Adam and Tom make a cake. T / F

## 3 Read and check ✓ or cross ✗.

1. It's seven o'clock.
2. This is Tom's cousin.
3. This is grandma.
4. Tom is happy.

## 4 Circle the odd one out.

1. cousin   aunt   cake
2. car   school   train
3. water   book   juice
4. Saturday   Adam   Julia

## 5 What do you think? Check ✓ and say.

|  | old | young | kind | funny | naughty |
| --- | --- | --- | --- | --- | --- |
| Adam is |  |  |  |  |  |
| Grandma is |  |  |  |  |  |
| Tom is |  |  |  |  |  |
| Mom is |  |  |  |  |  |

## 6 What happens next? → page 92

**I can** read a story about Tom's cousin.

# Phonics lab

CH AND SH

*I will learn the ch and sh sounds.*

**1** Write **ch**. Then point and say.

1 ____ips   2 ____ocolate
3 ____erries   4 ____eese

**2** Circle and say the words with the **sh** sound. Then write.

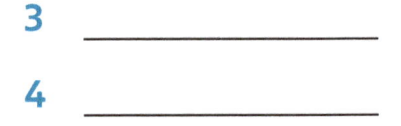

| s | a | r | x | i | n | c | h |
|---|---|---|---|---|---|---|---|
| h | d | s | h | i | r | t | e |
| i | j | e | g | d | z | f | c |
| p | t | x | a | c | y | s | w |
| q | u | r | k | u | b | h | q |
| s | h | e | l | f | v | o | l |
| c | b | m | w | o | i | p | d |
| j | e | t | h | f | a | k | g |
| x | s | h | o | e | s | n | p |
| d | y | l | u | b | o | r | h |
| t | s | m | s | h | e | e | p |

1 _____
2 _____
3 _____
4 _____
5 _____
6 _____

**3** Read and write **sh** or **ch**. Then listen and circle.

1 ____orts   ____oes   2 ____air   ____ess
3 ____icken   ____eese   4 ____irt   ____eep

**I can** use the ch and sh sounds.

# Experiment lab

**TECHNOLOGY: MILK**

*I will learn about making milk.*

## 1 Choose and write.

almonds   coconuts   cows   goats
horses   sheep   soya beans

| Animals | Plants |
|---|---|
|  |  |

## 2 Look and circle. Then read and check ✓ T (True) or F (False).

a         b

This is a  factory / store .

This is a  farmer / combine harvester .

|   | T | F |
|---|---|---|
| 1  We always get milk from animals. | ☐ | ☐ |
| 2  We sometimes get milk from plants. | ☐ | ☐ |
| 3  Farmers sometimes use combine harvesters. | ☐ | ☐ |
| 4  Stores make milk clean and healthy. | ☐ | ☐ |

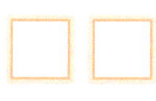

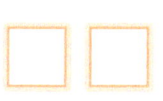

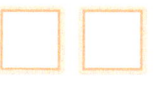

## EXPERIMENT TIME

### Report

**1 Circle, choose, and write.**

chocolate   ice   milk   salt
strawberry   sugar   vanilla

In my ice cream there is _____ from  an animal / a plant .

There is _____ and _____ .

There isn't any _____ .

**2 Check ✓ for you.**

I can make ice cream. ☐

I can't make ice cream. ☐

My ice cream is very good! ☐

My ice cream is not very good. ☐

**I know** about making milk.

# Language lab 2

**GRAMMAR 2: CAN I HAVE THIS / THAT ...?**

> I will ask and answer about objects using **this** / **that**.

## 1 Choose and write This ... or That ... .

ice cream   juice   salad

1. This salad
2. _____
3. _____
4. _____
5. _____
6. _____

## 2 Draw and color. Then write.

blue   green   orange   pink   purple   red   yellow

Draw a robot on the table. Draw a robot on the shelf.
Draw a ball on the table. Draw a ball on the shelf.

1  This robot is _____ .
2  _____ robot is _____ .
3  _____ ball is _____ .
4  _____ ball is _____ .

**I can** ask and answer using **this** / **that** .

# Let's order some food!

**COMMUNICATION**

*I will ask and answer about food.*

**1** 🎧 **Listen and check ✓.**

1 a    b

2 a    b

3 a    b

**2** 💬 **Look at 1. Ask and answer with a partner.**

- Can I have fish and pasta, please?
- Sure!
- Thank you.
- Can I have ice cream?
- Sorry, no.

**3** 💬 **Ask and answer with a partner. Check ✓ or cross ✗. Then draw.**

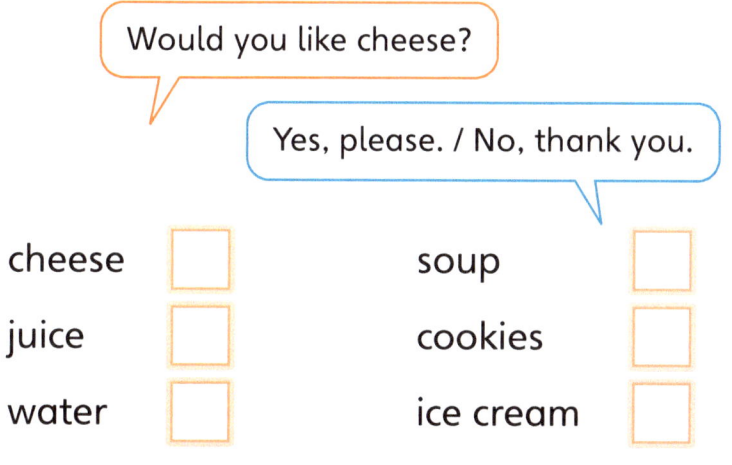

- Would you like cheese?
- Yes, please. / No, thank you.

cheese ☐    soup ☐
juice ☐     cookies ☐
water ☐     ice cream ☐

My partner would like …

**I can** ask and answer about food.

67

# PROJECT AND REVIEW — UNIT 5

Create a class meal

**Project report**

**1** Check ✓ or cross ✗ and write in the chart about your class meal.

| We have … | We draw the food | We make the food |
|---|---|---|
| chicken | | |
| bread | | |
| salad | | |
| water | | |

**2** Color the chart for your class. Then write.

**MATH ZONE**

Number of children
0   5   10   15   20   25

In my class …

_____ children like cheese.

_____ children like fish.

_____ children like ice cream.

_____ children like cookies.

**3** Draw your class meal and write.

This is our class meal.

We like _____ .

We don't like _____ .

**I can** create a class meal.

## 4 Look, read, and match.

a b c d e f

1. Can I have some cheese and salad, please?
   Yes, sure. Here you go.
   Can I have some juice?
   Would you like orange juice or tomato juice?
   Orange juice, please.
   ☐ ☐ ☐

2. Can I have some chicken and pasta, please?
   Sure.
   Can I have some juice?
   Would you like orange juice or tomato juice?
   Tomato juice, please.
   ☐ ☐ ☐

## 5 Read and color.

This soup is yellow. That soup is red.
That ice cream is green. This ice cream is pink.
This bread is brown. That bread is white.

1  2  3  4  5  6  7  8

## 6 Color the juice. Now point and say.

Can I have some juice, please?

This juice or that juice?

That juice. The green juice!

Now go to your progress chart on page 4.

# 6 Sports Day
### How can I organize a sports day?

**1** Choose and write. Then match.

jump   throw   run

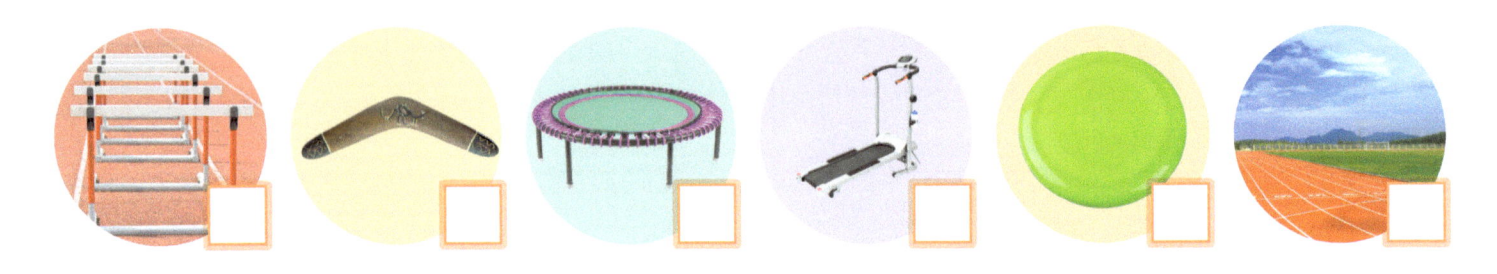

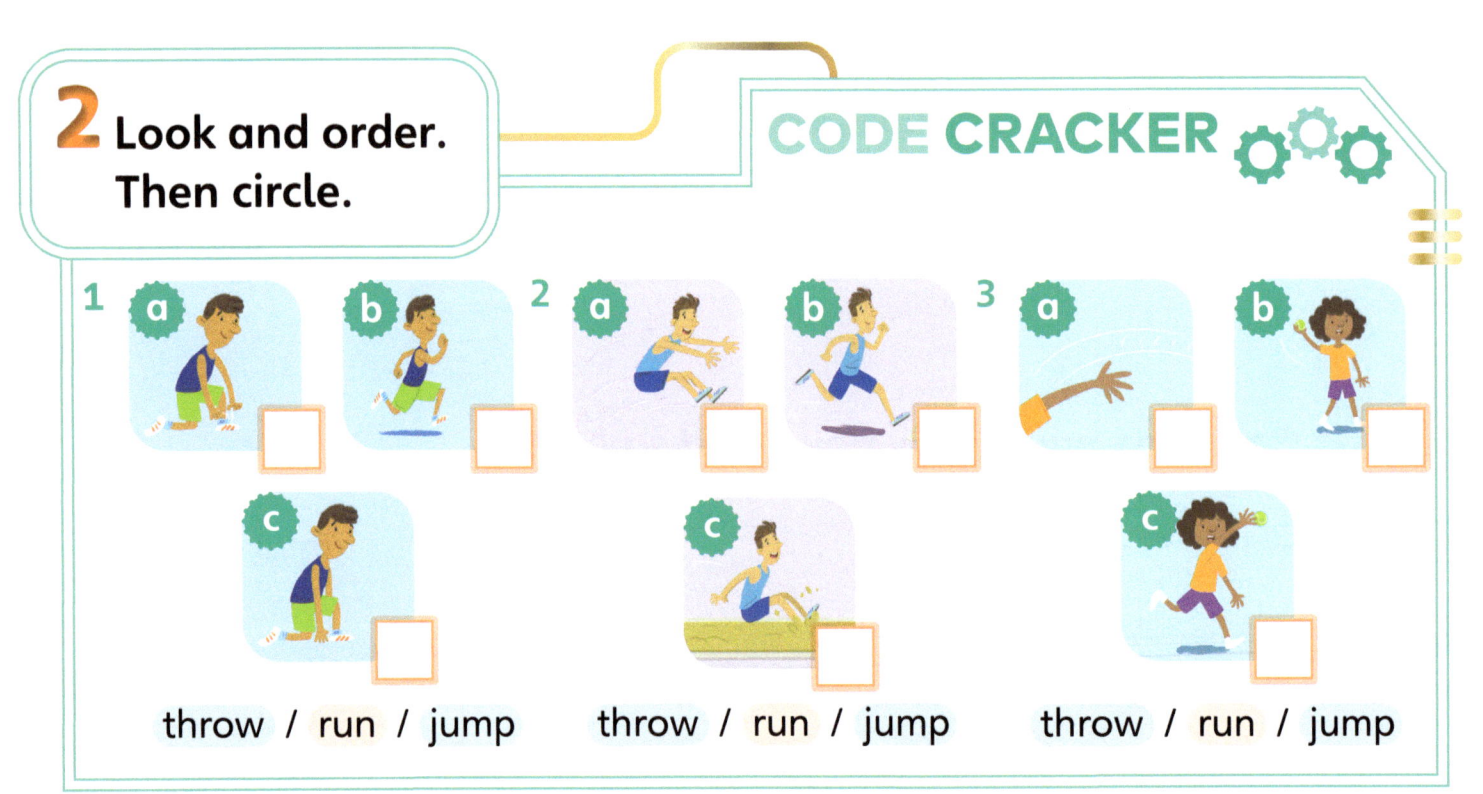

1 _____   2 _____   3 _____

**2** Look and order. Then circle.

## CODE CRACKER

1  a   b   c
throw / run / jump

2  a   b   c
throw / run / jump

3  a   b   c
throw / run / jump

# Do you play soccer?

VOCABULARY

*I will learn sport and activity words.*

## 1. Look, choose, and write.

> basketball   catch   hit   jump   kick   run   soccer
> team   throw   table tennis   volleyball   watch

1 _____   2 _____   3 _____   4 _____
5 _____   6 _____   7 _____   8 _____
9 _____   10 _____   11 _____   12 _____

**EXTRA VOCABULARY**

## 2. Look, listen, and say. Then match.

1 cricket    2 badminton    3 ice hockey

**I can** use sports and activity words.

# Language lab 1

**GRAMMAR 1: I'M JUMPING**

*I will talk about actions using I'm ...ing.*

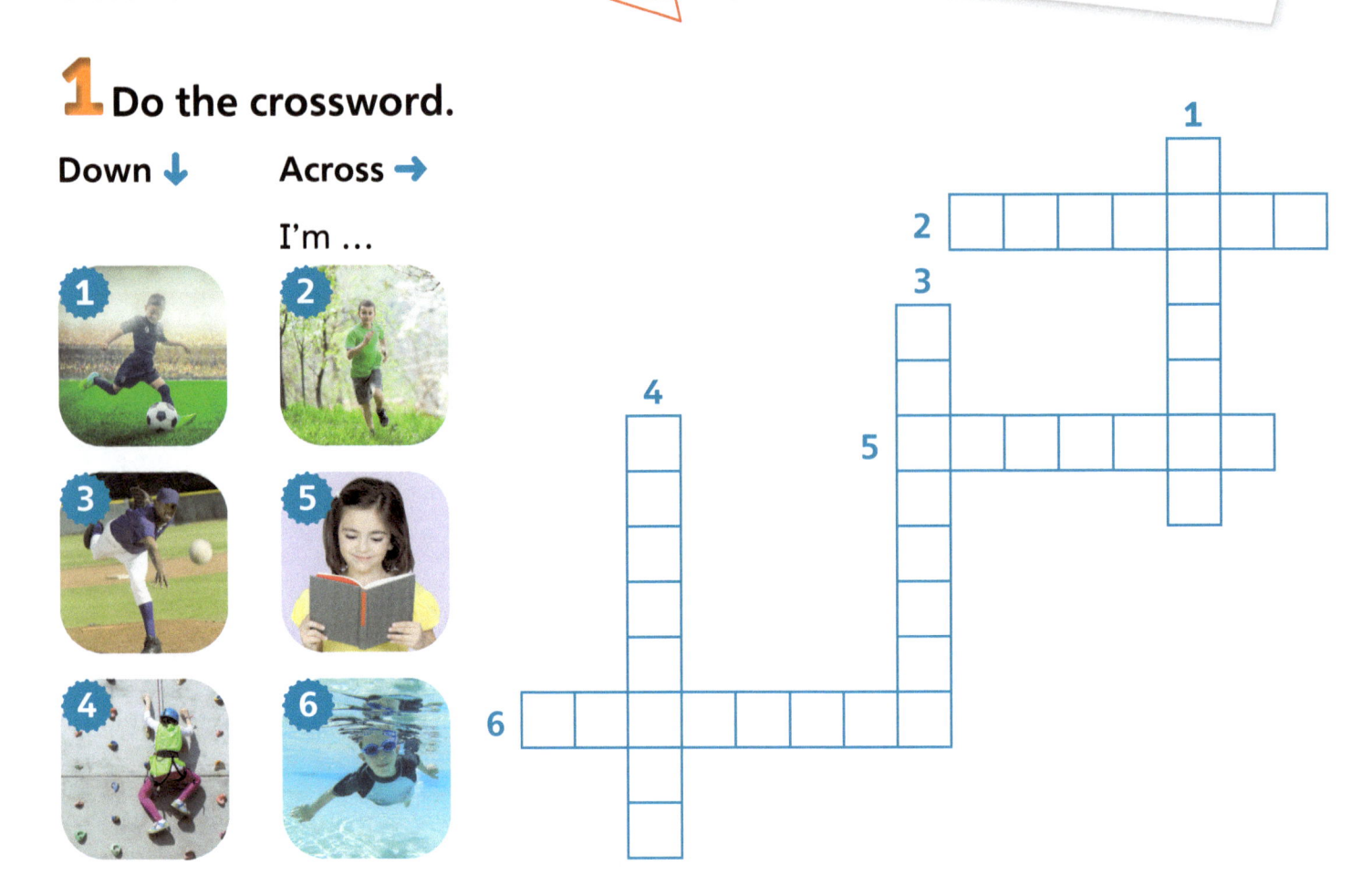

## 1 Do the crossword.

Down ↓   Across →

I'm ...

## 2 Write questions with Are you ...? Then listen and circle the correct answer.

1 (run) _____   Yes, I am. / No, I'm not.

2 (climb) _____   Yes, I am. / No, I'm not.

3 (swim) _____   Yes, I am. / No, I'm not.

4 (jump) _____   Yes, I am. / No, I'm not.

## 3 Write for you.

1 Are you reading now? _____

2 Are you running now? _____

Yes, I am.   No, I'm not.

## 4 Order and write.

1  volleyball   playing   .   I'm

_____

2  tennis   Are   ?   playing   you   table

_____

3  a   I'm   .   ball   kicking

_____

## 5 Check ☑ 2 sports and cross ☒ 2 sports. Then ask and answer with a partner.

| playing | watching |              |
|---------|----------|--------------|
|         |          | soccer       |
|         |          | volleyball   |
|         |          | table tennis |
|         |          | basketball   |

*I'm playing soccer. Are you playing soccer?*

*No, I'm not. I'm watching soccer.*

## 6 Now write about you and your partner.

**soccer**

1  I'm _____ .

   You're _____ .

**volleyball**

2  _____

   _____

**table tennis**

3  _____

   _____

**basketball**

4  _____

   _____

**I can** talk about actions using I'm …ing.

73

# Story lab

**READING**

*I will read a story about a game of soccer.*

## GOAL!

**1** Look, choose, and complete.

Are   not   running

1. Run, Anna! _____ you running, Leo?
   I'm _____!
   I'm _____ running. I'm jumping!

River   score

2. Goal!
   The _____ is _____ School 1, Castle School 1.

Kick   kicking

3. _____, Leo!
   I'm _____!

coming   leg

4. Ow! My _____!
   I'm _____, Leo!

## 2 Read and circle.

### ANOTHER GREAT GAME!

There are three / two teams; Green School and Castle School.

Leo is playing for Castle School. Leo is kicking / catching the ball.

Goal for Castle School!

Now a girl on the Green School team is / are running and kicking and … goal!

Now Leo is running and swimming / jumping … goal for Castle School.

Well done, Green School and Castle School. Bad / Great game!

## 3 Read again and write the score.

| Green School | Castle School |
|---|---|
| _____ | _____ |

## 4 Make a soccer game. Play with a partner.

Goal!

## 5 What happens next? ➡ page 93

**I can** read a story about a game of soccer.

# Phonics lab
TH

I will learn the **th** sounds.

**1** Write **th**. Then sing the song.

**SONG TIME**

Which do you want to play,
____is or ____at, ____is or ____at?
Which do you want to play,
____is or ____at, ____is or ____at?
Let's play all ____ese ____ings, 
Let's play all ____ese ____ings toge____er!

**2** Listen and number. Then say.

a  I can throw three things.
b  I can throw thirteen things.
c  I can throw these things!

**3** Write **th** and match.

1  ____ree
2  ____irteen
3  ____ank
4  ____row

**13**   **3**

**I can** use the **th** sounds.

76

# Experiment lab

MATH: MEASURING

*I will learn about measuring things in sports.*

## 1 Listen, choose, and write.

court   field   net

1. a table tennis _____
2. a soccer _____
3. a basketball _____

## 2 Listen and say.

20 30 40 50 60 70 80 90 100

twenty   thirty   forty
fifty   sixty   seventy
eighty   ninety
one hundred

## EXPERIMENT TIME

### Report

**1** How far can you blow? Color the graph.

MATH ZONE

**2** Now write the numbers in words.

I can blow the pencil _____ centimeters.

I can blow the tissue _____ centimeters.

I can blow the straw _____ centimeters.

**I know** about measuring things in sports.

# Language lab 2

**GRAMMAR 2: CAN YOU …?**

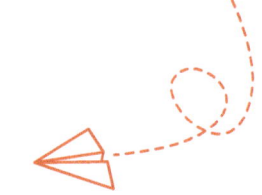

> I will ask and answer about actions using **Can you …?**

## 1 Read and match.

1 climb  2 play  3 catch  4 ride  5 jump  6 count

a bike   1 meter   table tennis   a tree   to 100   two balls

## 2 Complete the chart and write Yes, I can. or No, I can't. for you.

| Can you …? | | Yes, I can. / No, I can't. |
|---|---|---|
| _____ play table tennis? _____ | | _____ |
| _____ | | _____ |
| _____ | | _____ |
| _____ | | _____ |

## 3 Complete four questions with your own ideas. Then ask a partner and circle.

1  Can you play _____ ?  Yes, I can. / No, I can't.

2  Can you draw a _____ ?  Yes, I can. / No, I can't.

3  Can you _____ ?  Yes, I can. / No, I can't.

4  _____ ?  Yes, I can. / No, I can't.

---

**I can** ask and answer about actions using **Can you …?**

# Can you juggle?

COMMUNICATION

*I will talk about activities with my friends.*

**1** 🎧 034 **Listen and number.**

a  b  c  d  e  f

**2** Play the *Can you …?* game with a partner. Ask, try, then check ✓ or cross ✗.

| Can you … | Me | My partner |
|---|---|---|
| draw a cat with a hat? | ☐ | ☐ |
| jump and count to 20? | ☐ | ☐ |
| write three food words? | ☐ | ☐ |
| dance and say "five funny fish?" | ☐ | ☐ |

**I can** talk about activities with my friends.

# PROJECT AND REVIEW UNIT 6

Organize a Sports Day

Project report

**1** Check ✓ or cross ✗ and write in the chart for your Sports Day.

| Games | ✓ / ✗ | Who is playing? |
|---|---|---|
| Table tennis | | |
| Juggling | | |
| Yoga | | |
| Hula hoop | | |
| Basketball | | |
| Balloon volleyball | | |
| Sack race | | |

**2** Choose, circle, and write for you.

> juggling   playing balloon volleyball   playing soccer   watching

At our Sports Day ...

1   I'm / I'm not / My friend is / My friend isn't _____.
2   I'm / I'm not / My friend is / My friend isn't _____.
3   I'm / I'm not / My friend is / My friend isn't _____.
4   I'm / I'm not / My friend is / My friend isn't _____.

**I can** organize a Sports Day.

## 3 Draw and write.

My favorite game is table tennis.
I can hit the ball.
My favorite game is _____ .
I can _____ .

## 4 Read, choose, and complete.

> not   can   jumping   can't   dancing   tennis
> Are   playing   running   Can   Yes   Are

1  _____ you _____ soccer?

No, I'm _____ . I'm watching!

2  Are you _____ ?

_____ , I am! I _____ dance!

3  _____ you play _____ ?

No, I _____ !

4  _____ you _____ in the sack race?

No, I'm not! I'm _____ .

## 5 Play the *Can you catch and count …?* game with a partner.

20

40

30

Now go to your progress chart on page 4.

# Amazing boat races

CULTURE 3

**1** Find 6 words. Then choose and complete.

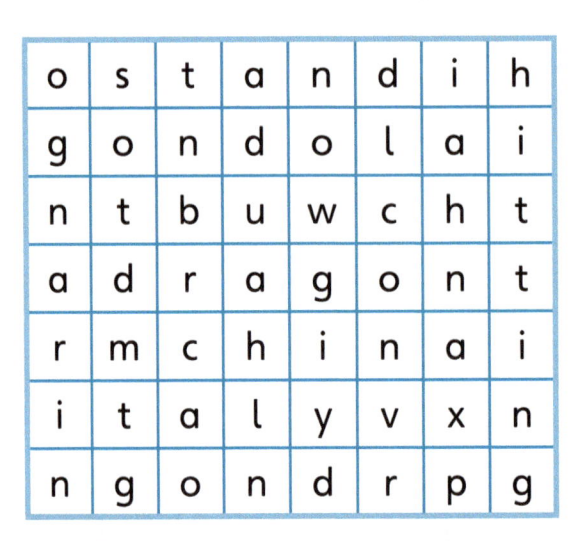

| o | s | t | a | n | d | i | h |
|---|---|---|---|---|---|---|---|
| g | o | n | d | o | l | a | i |
| n | t | b | u | w | c | h | t |
| a | d | r | a | g | o | n | t |
| r | m | c | h | i | n | a | i |
| i | t | a | l | y | v | x | n |
| n | g | o | n | d | r | p | g |

This is a _____ boat. It's in _____ . The man is _____ a drum.

This is a _____ . It's in _____ . You _____ up in the boats.

**2** Read and match.

1  The gondola race
2  The dragon boat race
3  The gondolas are red,
4  There are dragon heads

• is in June.
• yellow, silver, and gold.
• on the dragon boats.
• is in September.

## 3 Circle, write, and draw.

Look at this beautiful boat!

I'm in  China / Italy .

I'm watching a _____ race!

I'm eating _____ .

# Unit 2

Cut-outs

**A story about a town**

**A special day**

Draw a birthday cake for Castle Town.

Look! A _____!

Wow! _____ town is _____ today!

We're here, _____ Kelly!

Oh, _____! _____, Anna!

_____! I can't _____!

_____, Anna! I _____ hear music!

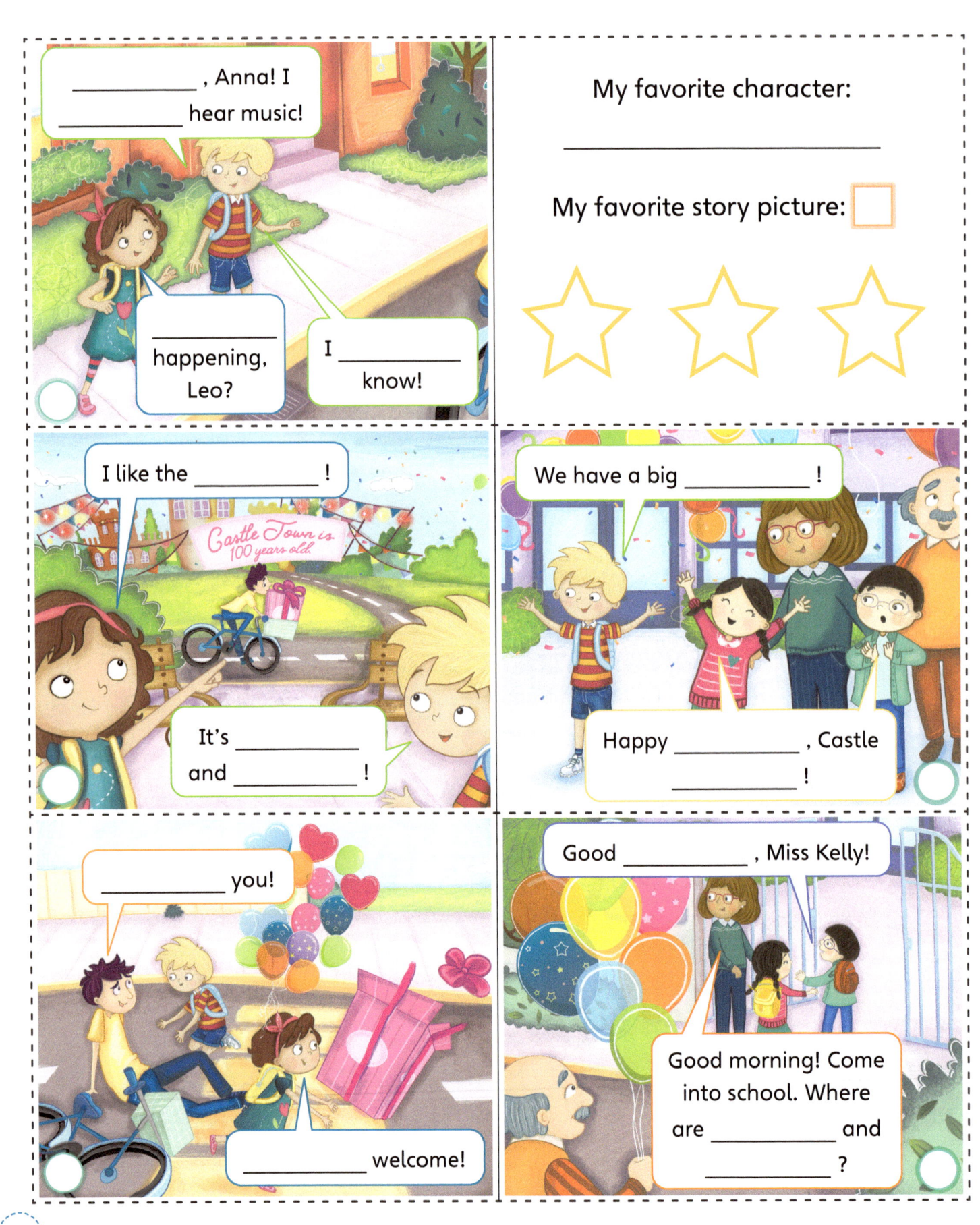

_____ happening, Leo?

I _____ know!

My favorite character:
_____

My favorite story picture: ☐

☆ ☆ ☆

I like the _____!

It's _____ and _____!

We have a big _____!

Happy _____, Castle _____!

_____ you!

_____ welcome!

Good _____, Miss Kelly!

Good morning! Come into school. Where are _____ and _____?

# Unit 3

Cut-outs

**A story about farm animals**

**Do goats dance?**

_____ , Mrs. Hay. What's happening?

I _____ know!

This is a _____ . Goats _____ grass and _____ .

Miss Kelly ... cows _____ and goats _____ !

_____ , Tom!

Look, _____ and _____ . This is a _____ . It eats grass.

87

**Draw your favorite animal.**

My favorite character: _____

My favorite story picture: ☐

☆ ☆ ☆

_____ goats _____ , Miss Kelly?

No, Tom! They _____ dance!

On the _____ !

To Mrs. Hay's _____ , please!

_____ cows _____ , Miss Kelly?

No, Tom. They _____ sing. They say " _____ !"

They _____ the music! They like _____ _____ !

# Unit 4

Cut-outs

## A story about a painting competition

## Who is this?

The _____ cup goes to … _____ !

Congratulations, Mr. Mud!

Who is this, Mrs. Hay?

It's my _____ .

Is she _____ ? She looks angry!

Er … no … she's _____ .

It's a rainbow! _____ , you are very _____ !

I have my _____ .

Great! I have _____ and crayons.

I have a _____ !

**Draw a rainbow.**

My favorite character:
_____

My favorite story picture: ☐

☆ ☆ ☆

This is very _____ , Mr. Mud!

Thank you! Milly is sometimes _____ , but she is _____ !

OK, finish _____ pictures now, _____ !

_____ is this, Tom?

It's my cousin. He's _____ naughty and _____ happy!

_____ _____ Milly!

90

# Unit 1
## Up and down!

**Look at the story on pages 10 and 11 in your Student's Book. What happens next? Check ✓ an ending then add your own idea.**

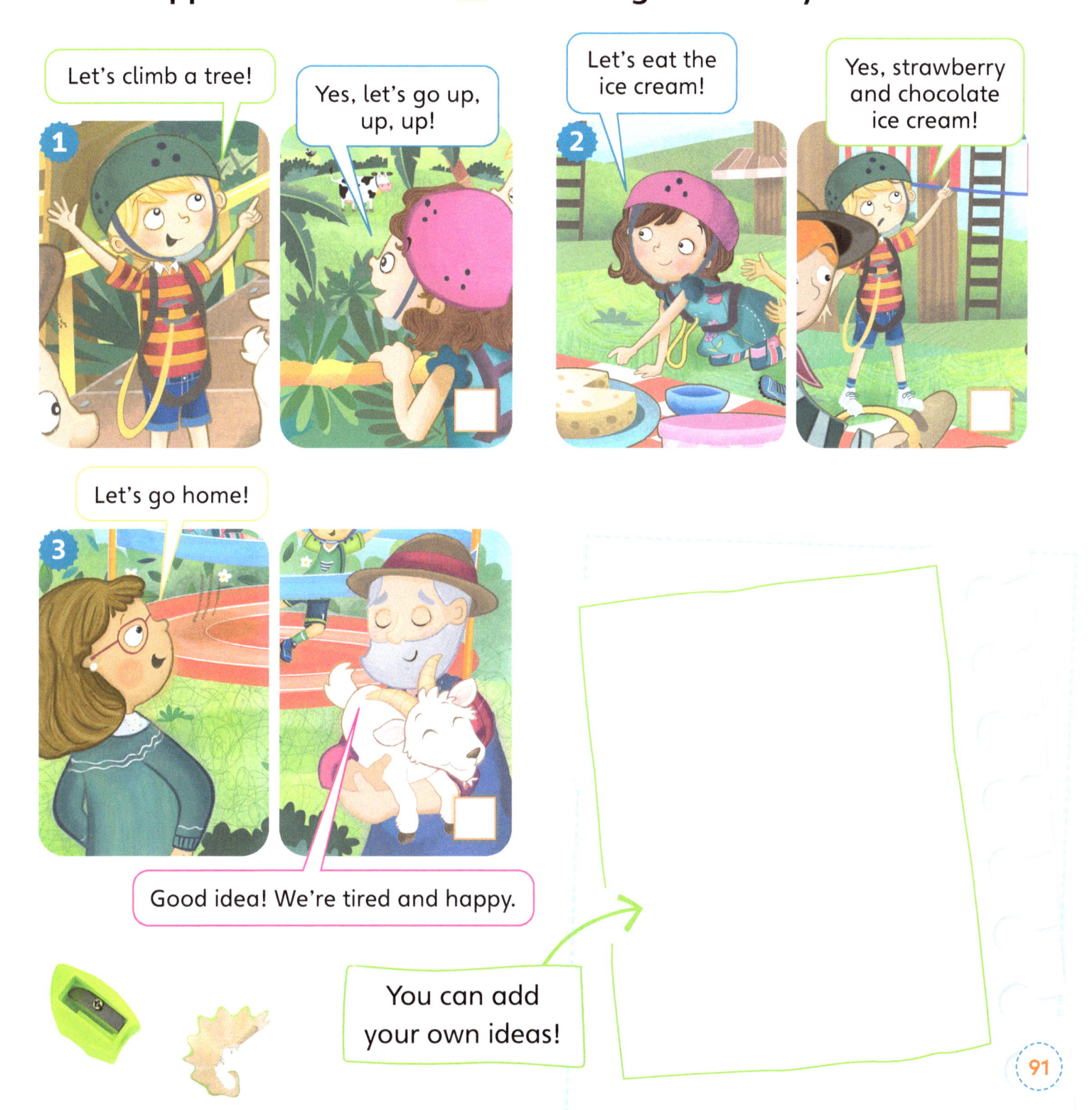

**1** Let's climb a tree!

Yes, let's go up, up, up!

**2** Let's eat the ice cream!

Yes, strawberry and chocolate ice cream!

**3** Let's go home!

Good idea! We're tired and happy.

You can add your own ideas!

# Unit 5

## Come over and play!

Look at the story on pages 70 and 71 of your Student's Book. What happens next? Check ✓ an ending then add your own idea.

**1.** Can I have some cake, please, Mom?

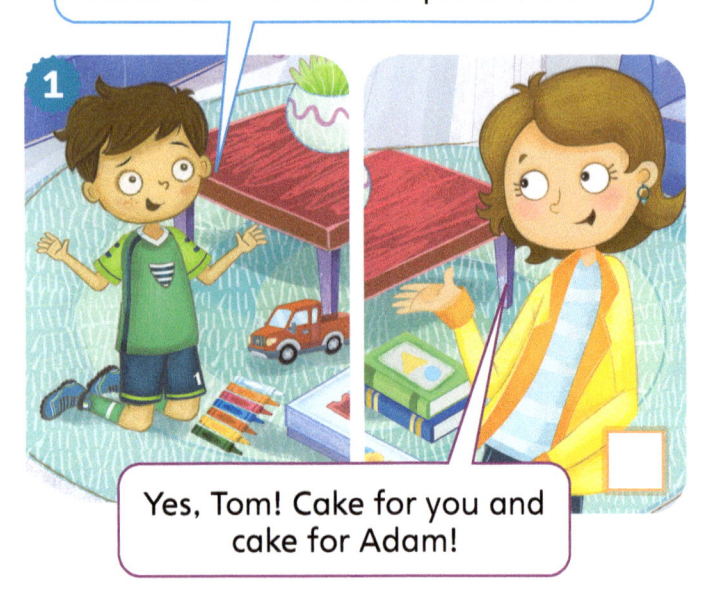

Yes, Tom! Cake for you and cake for Adam!

**2.** Goodbye!

Goodbye, Grandma! Goodbye, Aunt Julia! Goodbye, Adam!

**3.** Can I have your train, please, Tom?

Er … okay, Adam.

You can add your own ideas!

92

# Unit 6

## GOAL!

Look at the story on pages 84 and 85 of your Student's Book. What happens next? Check ✓ an ending then add your own idea.

**1**
- Milly, you're on Castle School team now!
- Run, Milly! Yes … goal!

**2**
- I'm playing table tennis with Milly!
- Good game, Milly!

**3**
- Milly's sleeping!
- Good night, Milly!

You can add your own ideas!